The Game
of Life

Words by Andrew Cope
Pics by Laura E Martin

Balloonview

Balloon View Ltd
Brenzett Place
Brenzett
Kent
TN29 0EE
www.balloonview.com

First published 2011 by Balloon View Ltd

Designed and set by
ALS Designs, Waterlooville, Hampshire.
www.als-designs.co.uk

Printed in India for Balloon View Ltd by
Replika Press Pvt. Ltd.

A catalogue for this book is available from the British Library.

ISBN-13: 978-1-907798-09-2

Nothing biting

Rhianna was fine. Well, as fine as any other teenager. School was OK. It was a bit of a drag to be honest. You know, all that coursework, homework and relationship stuff.

LIFE

MON	TUES	WED	THUR	FRI	SAT	SUN
OK	Rubbish	OK	OK	OK	Brilliant!	OK

Rhianna had brilliant days (she had a special name for them, 'Saturdays'). She had OK days too. And some were just rubbish, like Tuesdays for example, when she had maths, science, French and PE. Nightmare!

One day, out of the blue, Rhianna did some thinking. Some serious thinking.

She thought about her life. Fifteen years gone. If she looked after herself, Rhianna reckoned she could expect another 85 years. And, thought Rhianna, maybe I should aim higher than 'fine'?

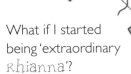

What if I started being 'extraordinary Rhianna'?

And what if I started now? Sure, I'd have to change a few things, but what would 'extraordinary Rhianna' look like?

And what would she sound like? And how would it feel to be my best self – always?

Rhianna wasn't convinced so she closed her eyes and ran two movies in her head. Movie one was a bit bleak. She imagined 'average Rhianna', and life seemed dreary. It was a black and white movie and, boy, was it dull!

Movie two was full colour 3-D 'Extraordinary Rhianna'. Thrills, excitement, fab career, great relationships and bags of fun. Wowza! Her decision was made. She was going to be her best self, always. It was what Rhianna called a 'no-brainer'.

So she did it. Rhianna changed!

Mr Jenkins noticed first. He handed out some maths homework and, predictably, the class groaned. Jamie rolled his eyes. Michelle said it wasn't fair. She explained to sir that she already had stacks of other work to do.

But Rhianna didn't groan. She smiled, because she knew that Mr J was giving homework so that she'd learn stuff that would help her get great grades. And great grades were the key to 'Extraordinary Rhianna's' next eighty-five years! On the way out she thanked Mr Jenkins for a great lesson.

Thank you Mr Jenkins!

'And I'll be doing the best homework I can,' she grinned. (Naturally, Mr Jenkins nearly fainted. He hot-footed it to the staffroom to spread the news).

Rhianna's extraordinary decision meant she got out of bed with more energy. She had purpose.

Her aim was to enjoy each day. To do her best. Not to waste it being wishy washy. For fifteen years she'd got out of bed because she *had* to. Her mum sometimes had to shout upstairs a dozen or more times! Imagine! Not any more. Because now Rhianna had decided to get out of bed because she *wanted* to.

And, because she'd decided to be extraordinary, she no longer stomped downstairs like a tousled haired grump monster. She was a pleasure to have at the brekky table!

9

Rhianna's positive approach meant she smiled more. Spooky stuff was happening. She noticed three massive things:

Firstly, school was fun and kind of easier. She couldn't quite explain why but she imagined it must be something to do with the fact that when she did her very best, she learned loads more.

Secondly, even Terrible Tuesday was cool!

And thirdly, people liked her more. It's not as though she'd been short of friends, but the extraordinary version of her was getting noticed. Her teachers were commenting. Her mum was delighted.

Even Danny had noticed her! Yikes!

Rhianna practiced being her best self until it became normal. In fact, after a few weeks, people started expecting her to be bright, cheery, enthusiastic and hard working. She felt great and, guess what, so did people who met her.

What a waste!

AVERAGE

She wondered why she'd spent 15 years being average. What a waste!

Of course, being positive about life didn't mean that rubbish things stopped happening. That would just be ridiculous. It still rained for example. And she still had to go to French (which she still didn't particularly like).

But she invented a game that she played in her head. Rhianna called it the 90/10 game.

I have a choice!

Rhianna figured that 90/10 was actually a game of life. It goes like this... 10% of whether Rhianna had a good day or bad day was down to circumstances. This 10% consisted of stuff that Rhianna couldn't control. Like French for example. Or the rubbish weather. Or homework. Or Mr Barker shouting in science. She figured that these things were going to happen to her anyway.

The 90% was more interesting. Rhianna figured that 90% of whether she had a good or bad day was down to how she reacted to the 10%.

So, when she lined up to go into French she thought, 'I can't control the lesson, but I can choose how to feel about it.' And, silly as it might sound, she began to feel positive about it. It was an opportunity to learn. Plus, it was only an hour.

And when the weather was rubbish (like nearly every day!) and everyone else was whinging, Rhianna applied the 90/10 principle.

'I can't control the weather,' she told herself, 'but I absolutely can choose to be positive about it.

I mean, some people live in the desert and would dance with joy if it rained this hard!'

And then there was homework. There was plenty of homework! And if there was an Olympics for moaning, she realised that a lot of her mates would be going for gold!

GO!

WHINGE   WHINGE   WHINGE

100   101   102

But not Rhianna. The 90/10 game of life meant she couldn't control the homework. It was coming whether she liked it or not. So she decided to like it. She attacked her homework with energy and enthusiasm. She handed it in a day early. And it was superb. Rhianna felt so proud.

OMG!

I can't control this

CHAT CHAT CHAT CHAT

QUIET!

And Mr Barker shouted less. At least at her.

Rhianna sat down, exhausted. All that dancing had worn her out. But, hey, it's good to dance at your 100th birthday bash.

Rhianna looked around at the smiling faces. Her eyes sparkled. Her laughter lines were deep. So many family and friends.

It's been an extraordinary journey!

The band started playing and everyone sang 'happy birthday'. Rhianna felt tears welling but now wasn't the time. She blew out the 100 candles with one breath and the room filled with laughter and applause.

'Quiet please, I have a few words to say about the birthday girl,' announced Danny.

He stood by his wife and held her hand. His thumb rubbed her wrinkles and then squeezed tight. He smiled at his beautiful wife. She beamed back. Rhianna's mind went back to her decision, 85 years ago.

An extraordinary decision, she thought. And an extraordinary life!

Thinking time...

Rhianna's story is based on research into happiness and positivity. To cut an incredibly long story short, you can learn to be positive. And having a positive, confident and upbeat approach to life will get you better results at home, at work, on holiday and even in Asda.

The problem is, it's a lot easier to be negative! People can get stuck in whinge mode. I've met some who've become experts at it, honing their negative powers for 50 or more years!

The great news is that the earlier you get into positive habits the better it is for you and all those around you. So here are a few things to think about:

1. What's the key to Rhianna's success?

2. Imagine you are an alien visiting planet earth. Your mission is to find the secret of 'happiness' and take it back to your planet. What 'secret' would you take back?

3. Run 2 movies in your head:

Movie 1 is a black and white film of the 'average' you. Close your eyes and picture your future. What job and relationships do you have? Where does the average you live? How does the average you walk and talk? How much does the average you smile?

Movie 2 is the full colour 3D 'extraordinary' you. Go on, run the movie! Check out your future now. You'll see a definite increase in the smile rate!

4. What's the key to your successful future?

5. What 3 things will you do to load life in your favour?

6. What 3 things will you stop doing to improve your lot?

7. Imagine you are 30 years old and life has been great. Complete the following sentence in less than 20 words:

'I've achieved some great things because...'

8. Most of us have been touched deeply by a few important people; people who, because of their feelings for us have helped us become who we are today. Some of what these special people gave to us was uplifting and inspiring. Sometimes, we didn't really appreciate them, until now! Maybe they worked during the day and looked after the household too. Maybe they gave us time. They helped us get through difficult times, or offered good advice. Maybe it's a teacher, or parent, or grandparent, or a friend?

Write a letter to this person. Tell the person what he or she has done for you, the impact they've had and how grateful you are. Tell them what you've learned from them. Write from your heart.

9. Send it.

Andy Cope

Andy Cope (it's only his mum who calls him 'Andrew') lives with his wife and two children (Sophie and Ollie) in a village near Derby, England. He was born the same year that England won the world cup.

Like many authors, he has a proper job that keeps him busy during the day and he writes furiously in his spare time. Andy is a qualified teacher who used to work as a lecturer in Colleges and Universities but he now works for himself training teenagers, teachers, managers and business people. He runs a really fab course called 'The Art of Being Brilliant', which is about positive psychology and generally being the best person you can be. His work takes him all over the world.

Andy has written the highly successful 'Spy Dog' and 'Spy Pups' series for Puffin. His first book won the Red House Children's Book Award and he is currently working on picture books for the under 6s. Andy has also written 'Being Brilliant' and 'The Art of Being Brilliant' aimed at mums, dads and business people. He's also penned 'A Brilliant Life' which is the UK's first positive psychology books for teenagers.

Andy has done numerous TV and radio appearances. He has also set up the hugely successful 2%ers club, the UK's first, foremost and...err...only society for happy people.

One of Andy's ambitions is to be able to surf, brilliantly.

www.artofbrilliance.co.uk

23

Other great books by Andy Cope

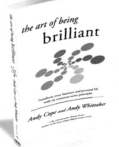

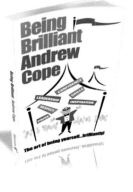